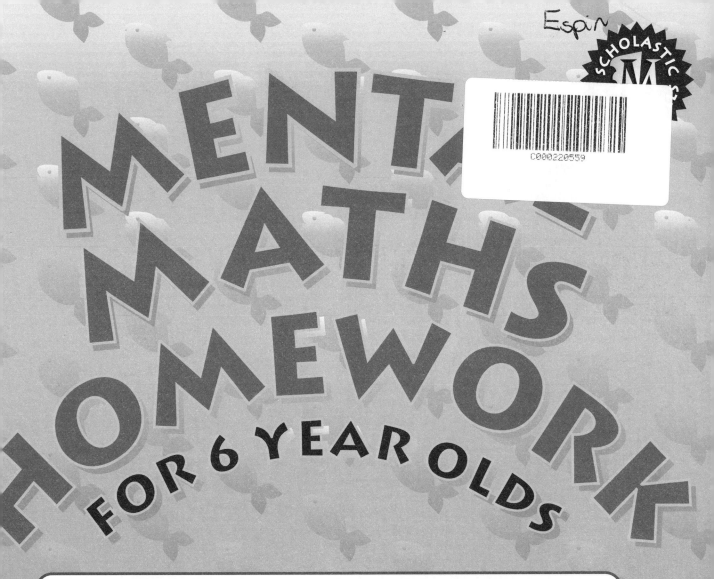

MENTAL MATHS HOMEWORK

FOR 6 YEAR OLDS

Espin

C000220559

SERIES EDITOR
Lin Taylor
The IMPACT Project, University of
North London Enterprises Ltd

AUTHOR
Helen Williams

EDITOR
Joel Lane

ASSISTANT EDITOR
Clare Miller

SERIES DESIGNER
Anna Oliwa

DESIGNER
Mark Udall

ILLUSTRATIONS
Jenny Tulip

COVER ARTWORK
James Alexander/David Oliver
Berkeley Studios

Text © 1999 Helen Williams
© 1999 Scholastic Ltd

Designed using Adobe Pagemaker
Published by Scholastic Ltd, Villiers House, Clarendon
Avenue, Leamington Spa, Warwickshire CV32 5PR

1 2 3 4 5 6 7 8 9 0   9 1 2 3 4 5 6 7 8 0

British Library Cataloguing-in-Publication Data
A catalogue record for this book is available from the
British Library.

ISBN 0-439-01702-5

CONTENTS

IMPACT

ABOUT HOMEWORK

Homework can be a very useful opportunity to practise and develop children's understanding of the work done in school. Games and maths challenges can be very good activities to share with someone at home, especially to develop mental maths strategies and maths language skills. Research* indicates that parental involvement is a major factor in children's educational success. Most parents want to help their children with their school work, but often do not know how and 'traditional' homework does not involve parents. Shared homework activities, such as can be found in *Mental Maths Homework*, are designed to be completed with a parent or helper, such as a sibling, neighbour or other adult who can work with the child. Working one-to-one with an adult in the home environment really has a powerful effect. The National Numeracy Strategy strongly supports this type of homework, which is in line with a variety of government guidelines on the role of parents and making home links.

ABOUT MENTAL MATHS AT HOME

Mental Maths Homework is particularly concerned to develop children's *mental* mathematics. In order to become competent at mental calculation, children need to talk about mathematics and try out different strategies, as well as to practise number facts and skills. Children explaining their mathematics to a parent or helper can help to clarify and develop their understanding of the mathematics. This type of homework, developed by The IMPACT Project, is a *joint* activity: the helper and child working together.

ABOUT MENTAL MATHS HOMEWORK

This series comprises of six books, one for each age group from 6–11 years (Year 1/P2–Year 6/P7). Each book contains 36 photocopiable activities – enough for one to be sent home each week throughout the school year, if you wish. The activities concentrate on the number system and developing children's calculation strategies and are designed to fit into your planning, whatever scheme you are using. Since these books are designed to support the same aims of developing mental maths strategies and vocabulary, they make an ideal follow-on to the class work outlined in Scholastic's other *Mental Maths* series. The objectives for each activity are based on those in the National Numeracy Strategy *Framework for Teaching Mathematics* and the content is appropriate for teachers following other UK curriculum documents.

USING THE ACTIVITIES IN SCHOOL

Although the books are designed for a particular age group they should be used flexibly so that the right level of activity is set for a child or class. All the activities are photocopiable: most are one page, some are two, or require an extra resource page (to be found at the back of the book) for certain games or number card activities. The activities for older children will generally take longer than those for younger children.

BEFORE

It is essential that each activity is introduced to the class before it is sent home with them. This fulfils several crucial functions. It enables the child to explain the activity to the parent or carer; ensuring the child understands the task. It also familiarises the child with the activity; developing motivation and making the activity more accessible. This initial introduction to the activity can be done as part of a regular maths lesson, at the end of the day, or whenever will fit most appropriately into your class's routine.

AFTER

It is also important that the child brings something back to school from the activity at home. This will not necessarily be substantial, or even anything written, since the homework activities aim to develop mental mathematics. It is equally important that what the child brings in from home is genuinely valued by you. It is unlikely that parents will be encouraged to share activities with their children if they do not feel that their role is valued either. Each activity indicates what should be brought back to school, and the teachers' notes (on pages 5–8) offer guidance on introducing and working with or reviewing the outcome of each activity.

HELPERS

All the activities have a note to the helper explaining the purpose of the activity and how to help the child, often emphasizing useful vocabulary. The helpers' notes also give indications of how to adapt the activity at home, and what to do if the child gets stuck. Many of the activities are games or fun activities which it is hoped that the parent and child will enjoy doing together and will do again, even when not set for homework, thus increasing the educational benefit. It is particularly beneficial for a game to be played a number of times.

OTHER WAYS TO USE THE ACTIVITIES

The activities offered in *Mental Maths Homework* are very flexible and will be used in different ways in different schools. As well as being used for shared homework, they could form the basis of a display or a school challenge, or be used as activities for a maths club. Or, they could be used independently of the school situation by parents who wish to provide stimulating and appropriate educational activities for their children.

USING THE ACTIVITIES AT HOME

If you are a parent using these activities outside of school:
● Choose an activity you both think looks interesting and get going straight away with your child. Make the work *joint*: the helper and the child working out what has to be done *together*.
● Read the instructions to your child and ask him or her to explain what has to be done. It is very effective for the child to do the explaining.

USING HOMEWORK DIARIES

Developing a dialogue between teacher and parent is an important part of shared homework. By working with the child at home, the parent becomes more familiar with the mathematics of the classroom. The teacher also needs to hear from the parent about how the child is faring with the activities. Diaries provide a very good mechanism for this. The helpers and/or the children can comment on the activities (which will give you important feedback) and individual targets can be put into the diary. The diaries can act, therefore, as an important channel of communication. (See below for details about finding out more information about diaries.)

ABOUT THIS BOOK

The IMPACT homework activities that follow are planned to reflect the content of both the National Curriculum for Mathematics and the *National Numeracy Framework* for children aged 5–6 years. Objectives drawn from the *National Numeracy Framework* for Year 1 are referred to in the Teachers' notes for each activity.

The activities are not presented in order of difficulty and reflect the breadth of one year's number work with a Year 1 class. The balance of activities for Year 1 is towards counting and ordering. This is because counting and awareness of our number system underpins children's understanding of number. Counting, not only to establish quantity but also to learn the order of the words, is crucial to understanding number. In order for the regularity of our number system to become apparent to children, they will need to: count aloud regularly and 20 and preferably above 60 (where the aural pattern is regular – six-ty = six tens); and see numbers in position, for example on a 0–100 number line, to be able to distinguish between numbers like 16 and 60 when spoken. This book is aimed at improving a child's **mental** mathematics, so very little is recorded formally and children should be encouraged not to do their working out on paper.

The IMPACT activities in this book often involve learning and playing a simple dice, domino or card game. One of the advantages of playing a game at home as well as at school is that it is played more often. It is only after a game has become more familiar that children are able to answer searching questions about the effect of different rules, and are able to predict what might happen. This rule and pattern-searching is the essence of mathematical activity at all ages. Using games as home activities gives us more time and opportunity to discuss the strategies.

* Bastiani, J. & Wolfendale, S. (1996) *Home-School Work: Review, Reflection and Development* David Fulton Publishers.

THE IMPACT PROJECT

The activities in *Mental Maths Homework* have all been devised by members of The IMPACT Project, based at the University of North London. The project, a pioneer of shared homework, with a wealth of experience, is involved in a variety of initiatives concerning parental involvement and homework. It also supports schools in setting up a school framework for shared homework. If you would like help with developing shared homework, planning a whole-school framework for homework or developing mental mathematics at home and at school, maybe through INSET with experienced providers, contact The IMPACT Project. Information about other activities undertaken by the project and about other IMPACT books and resources, such as the IMPACT diaries, is also available from The IMPACT Project.

The IMPACT Project
University of North London
School of Education
166–220 Holloway Road
London
N7 8DB

tel. no. 020 7753 7052

fax. no. 020 7753 5420

e-mail: impact-enquiries@unl.ac.uk
impact-orders@unl.ac.uk

web: http://www.unl.ac.uk/impact

COUNTING & ORDERING

MY NUMBER TRACK

OBJECTIVES: To say, read and write numbers to at least 20. To compare and order some two-digit numbers.

BEFORE: Look at, and discuss, different numbers on the class number line. Ask: *Who can read this number? Which number have I covered?*

AFTER: Allow time for the children to show and tell each other about their number tracks. Look at the difference between a number **track** (numbers in spaces) and a number **line** (numbers on points on a line). Use the children's tracks to invent games.

STAND UP, SIT DOWN

OBJECTIVES: To say the number names to 29 in order, forwards and backwards. To begin to recognize odd and even numbers.

BEFORE: Do the activity as a class.

AFTER: This activity leads into many different counting activities. You might try: counting from and back to different starting points together; sitting and counting silently to 2, standing and counting aloud to 4, then sitting and counting silently to 6, and so on.

OUT AND ABOUT NUMBERS

OBJECTIVES: To read numerals in a variety of contexts. To use the vocabulary of comparing and ordering.

BEFORE: Allow longer than a week for this. Discuss where you might see numbers outside school, and what they are 'for'. Many numbers 'label' something (such as a bus) instead of referring to an amount.

AFTER: Allow the children time to tell each other about the numbers they have found. Order the numbers: *Have we brought in all the numbers to 20?* Look at numerals in other scripts: Chinese, Punjabi and so on.

RACE TO 20

OBJECTIVES: To count at least 20 objects reliably. To use the vocabulary of comparing numbers.

BEFORE: Demonstrate the game.

AFTER: Replay the game with a group of children. Play other counting games with dice, such as filling a box with marbles and then emptying it.

FILL IT

OBJECTIVES: To use the vocabulary of estimation. To give a sensible estimate of up to 30 objects. To count at least 20 objects accurately.

BEFORE: Discuss what an estimate is. Ask the children how many small bricks they think your hand holds, then show them.

AFTER: Let the children discuss what they have found out in groups. *How can we decide whose pot or box is larger?* Have a class 'estimate and count' table with a new number every day.

DOT-TO-DOT

OBJECTIVES: To read and order numbers to 30. To use the vocabulary of ordering and comparing.

BEFORE: Do the preliminary counting activity.

AFTER: Look at the completed sheets together. Invent new dot-to-dot puzzles to focus on different parts of the number system. The children could draw their own puzzles, using squared paper.

LADDERS

OBJECTIVES: To order numbers to 10 and position them on a number track. To read and write numbers. To use the vocabulary of comparing and ordering.

BEFORE: Demonstrate the game.

AFTER: Discuss what happened when the children played the game at home. Use a version of the game to order three non-consecutive numbers: draw ladders with only three rungs and play with cards to 10; turn over three cards, one at a time, each time deciding where to write the number on the ladder.

RACE THE NUMBERS

OBJECTIVES: To read and write numbers. To say which of two numbers is more or less. To use the vocabulary of comparing and ordering.

BEFORE: Demonstrate the game. You do not need to play to the end.

AFTER: This game provides an opportunity to discuss ideas of probability. Replay the game in pairs and compare the children's sheets to see which numbers won. Can the children explain why some numbers are more likely to win than others? What will happen if you play with two packs of cards?

SHAKE, GUESS AND COUNT

OBJECTIVES: To count at least 20 objects reliably. To use the vocabulary of estimation. To give a sensible estimate of a number of objects.

BEFORE: Play the game with the class a few times.

AFTER: Encourage the children to 'shake, guess and count' each other's containers. Have an 'All these are 5' or 'All these are 20' table display, with different-sized items or pictures of the same amount arranged in different ways. Include one container or picture that has 'the odd number out'.

TEENY MONEY

OBJECTIVES: To begin to partition two-digit numbers into tens and ones. To count on in ones from 10. To know 10 more and 10 less than a given number.

BEFORE: Lay out an amount in pennies and ask the children how much is there. Remind them that a 10p coin is worth ten pennies. Count in tens using 10ps.

AFTER: Let the children share and discuss their coin drawings in pairs or small groups. Talk about the tens and ones making up each number. Make the same numbers with Base 10 apparatus or Cuisenaire tens and ones. If appropriate, start with two 10p coins and count on in pennies from 20p.

ADD 10 OR ADD 1

OBJECTIVES: To know the number that is 1 or 10 more or less than any number to 20. To read numbers to 10.
BEFORE: Play the game with the class, with you as the number-person and the children as the add-person. Talk about how you are adding 10, and relate this to a number line or number square.
AFTER: Encourage the children to talk about what they found harder and easier. Play using coins; or using the black cards to add and the red cards to subtract.

ORDER AND CHANGE

OBJECTIVES: To order the numbers from 0 to 10. To count up to 10 objects reliably. To use the vocabulary of ordering and comparing, and of time.
BEFORE: Talk through the activity. Demonstrate laying the 0–10 cards in order and placing the items underneath them. Play the 'hide and change' game.
AFTER: Try ordering cards against a timer, forwards and backwards with different sequences of numbers. Investigate patterns of numbers: *How many different ways can you arrange 5 pegs in a pegboard?* Discuss what counts as a 'different' arrangement.

FOLLOW ON

OBJECTIVES: To order the numbers from 0 to 10. To use the vocabulary of ordering numbers.
BEFORE: Use one suit of cards to order 0–10 with the class, then ask questions: *Which number is between 3 and 5? Which number is 1 less than 9?*
AFTER: Let the children talk about what happened and display their lists of ordered cards. Replay the game, but order the cards backwards from 10. If appropriate, play with a different set of number cards.

WRITE IT IN

OBJECTIVES: To recognize and predict from simple number patterns. To reason and explain orally. To use the vocabulary of ordering numbers. To read and write numbers to 25.
BEFORE: Look at and talk about some of the patterns on a 0–99 or 1–100 grid. Draw a large 5 × 5 grid on the board and start to fill it in with the class.
AFTER: Encourage the children to talk about their completed number grids. Then ask children to describe the positions of different numbers as 'between', 'before', 'after' and so on.

ADDITION & SUBTRACTION

TAKE ME AWAY

OBJECTIVES: To reason orally. To understand the operation of subtraction and the related vocabulary.
BEFORE: Demonstrate the game to the class.
AFTER: Encourage the children to talk about the game. Play in groups of three or four, with a new rule:

fill your line with red, blue and green counters. You can choose how many of each colour. At each turn, you can remove only counters in **one** colour. Miss a turn if you do not have enough counters to remove.

EGG BOXES

OBJECTIVES: To reason orally. To understand the operation of addition and the related vocabulary.
BEFORE: Demonstrate the game by rolling a dice and filling one egg box. Discuss the instructions. Let the children decide how many boxes to play with.
AFTER: Encourage the children to talk about what they have done. Make some playdough eggs in two colours, then play this game: roll one dotted (or number) dice and one colour dice to tell you how to fill the egg box. Look at the filled box and say what addition you see. Play again, using three colours.

TWO-COUNTER RACE

OBJECTIVES: To understand the operation of addition. To recognize that additions can be done in any order. To reason orally. To practise addition facts to 10.
BEFORE: Use a large version of part of the grid to demonstrate the game. Turn over one card at a time, so that the children can count the black number of moves and then add on the red number. Ask them to talk you through the rest of the game.
AFTER: Replay the game in small groups. List the number pairs using red and black pens, both ways round (as in 2, 3 and 3, 2). Play the game with one counter and identify the larger number to move first.

FINGERS FIVE

OBJECTIVES: To add numbers by counting on, and by partitioning and recombining. To practise addition facts to 10.
BEFORE: 'Flash' some fingers for the children to tell you how many without counting. Work through the initial task of showing 7, 8 and 9 fingers in different ways.
AFTER: Sort and display the children's drawings of their hands or the numbers they made. Use Cuisenaire rods to make the numbers to 10 as '5 and something'.

FIND THE TENS

OBJECTIVES: To begin to know pairs of numbers totalling 10. To recognize an addition pattern.
BEFORE: With the class, show the pairs of numbers that total 10 by folding some fingers and leaving some upright. Find pairs of playing cards that make 10.
AFTER: Encourage the children to compare and talk about their addition patterns. Display these. Replay the game as a memory game: turn the cards face down, then take turns to turn over two cards. If the pair total 10, keep them; if not, turn them back.

ADD THEM ALL UP

OBJECTIVES: To choose and use appropriate mental strategies for addition, such as using known number pairs and counting on.

BEFORE: Practise turning over three cards and discussing different ways to add the numbers. Which number pairs do children recognize straight away?
AFTER: Share the number-pairs that different children know by heart. Replay the game, turning over four cards instead of three.

FIND THE DIFFERENCE

OBJECTIVES: To understand subtraction as 'finding the difference'. To use vocabulary related to subtraction.
BEFORE: This activity is complementary to 'Add them all up'. Make sure the children know what 'difference' means; you could show them with two Cuisenaire rods (or sticks of Unifix) laid alongside each other. If necessary, demonstrate the game.
AFTER: Encourage the children to talk about their experiences of playing the game, and to say what differences they know by heart. Replay the game, but turn over three cards and choose two to subtract.

CALENDAR COUNTDOWN

OBJECTIVES: To understand subtraction as 'taking away'. To use vocabulary related to subtraction. To compare numbers. To use vocabulary related to time.
BEFORE: This activity takes place over a few weeks. It is best sent home at the beginning of a new month. Discuss what is happening at school in the next few weeks. Collect some calendars for the children to look at and discuss. Prepare a large class calendar.
AFTER: As the children bring in their 'big day' dates, enter them onto the class calendar. Discuss whose big day has passed, whose is still to come, who has waited the longest and so on.

DOMINO DOUBLES

OBJECTIVES: To recognize doubles and near-doubles. To choose and use appropriate operations and mental strategies to solve problems. To recognize and predict from simple number patterns.
BEFORE: Look at a set of dominoes with the children. Discuss the patterns and the numbers.
AFTER: Look at, sort and display the children's drawings of doubles and near-doubles. Try calling out any even number to 12: how quickly can the children tell you which double domino makes that total?

NO TENS ALLOWED

OBJECTIVES: To add more than two numbers together. To look for numbers which total 10. To choose suitable operations and mental strategies to solve problems.
BEFORE: Practise adding three or four small numbers, using the 1–3 cards needed for the game. Discuss addition strategies such as: looking for the largest number and counting on; holding a running total in your head to add on to.
AFTER: Replay the game in groups of three or four (you will need more than one pack of cards). Use the 4- and 5-cards. Encourage the children to talk about how they add up more than two numbers mentally.

FLIP AND MOVE

OBJECTIVES: To understand addition and subtraction and use the related vocabulary. To say the number that is 1 more or 1 less than any number to 20.
BEFORE: Demonstrate the game. It might help to label the sides of the coin '1' and '2'.
AFTER: Encourage the children to talk about the game. Replay the game, racing back from the end of the track by **taking away** 2 for a head and 1 for a tail. Try playing on an unnumbered board, with children writing in the numbers as they land on them.

MULTIPLICATION & DIVISION

FAIR TOWERS

OBJECTIVES: To count objects reliably. To read numbers. To count on in 2s. To begin to recognize odd and even numbers.
BEFORE: Using Lego, Multilink or Unifix, demonstrate taking a card and seeing whether the number will divide into two equal towers. Ask: *How will we know whether they are equal?*
AFTER: Encourage the children to talk about their lists of numbers that 'fair shared'. Find the numbers on your class number line. What do the children notice? Replay the game, allowing individual children to choose cards. This will tell you whether they can recognize the even numbers. If appropriate, play with numbers above 10.

COIN TOSS

OBJECTIVES: To count on in twos. To compare amounts of money. To begin to recognize even numbers.
BEFORE: Count to 10, asking the class to stand when you say the odd numbers and sit when you say the even numbers. Count backwards in the same way. Remind the children of the value of a 2p coin. Count a row of 2p coins aloud together.
AFTER: Encourage the children to talk about their lists of numbers and to explain how these relate to the coins. Display these lists. Replay the game, using 5p or 10p coins to count in 5s or 10s.

EVERY THIRD

OBJECTIVES: To recognize and predict from simple number patterns. To reason and explain orally. To begin to count on in steps of 3. To use the language of ordering numbers.
BEFORE: Draw a large grid on the board (different from the grid on the homework sheet) and number it from 1. Tell the children to keep silent until you give a signal. Without saying anything, start colouring in every third square. Halfway through, give the signal and ask the children to describe what you are doing.
AFTER: Encourage the children to discuss and compare their sheets. Read the coloured-in numbers

together, forwards and backwards. Cover a coloured-in number: can the children say which one it is? Try colouring in every third square on various different grids. Go above 30 if appropriate.

EVERY FIFTH
OBJECTIVES: To recognize and predict using simple patterns. To reason and explain orally. To count on in steps of 5. To use the language of ordering numbers.
BEFORE: See notes for 'Every third'.
AFTER: See notes for 'Every third'; continue the pattern to 100 if appropriate. List the numbers as the children read them. What do they notice? Display the list.

MULTISTEP & MIXED OPERATIONS

MY CALENDAR
OBJECTIVES: To say, read and write numbers to 30. To compare and order two-digit numbers. To use vocabulary related to time.
BEFORE: Together, look at an empty calendar sheet (page 40) and discuss what it is. Label each child's sheet with his or her birthday month.
AFTER: Encourage each child to talk about his or her calendar sheet and the patterns of the days and numbers. Use these sheets to make a class year calendar. Mark the days of the week and any important events. Set time problems regularly: *How long is it until...? How long ago did we...?*

6 SPOTS
OBJECTIVES: To practise addition and subtraction facts to 6. To choose and use appropriate operations and mental strategies to solve problems. To recognize and predict from simple patterns and relationships.
BEFORE: Look together at a set of dominoes. Discuss the numbers and remind the children how to play the traditional dominoes game. List some pairs of numbers that total 6. Relate these to the dominoes.
AFTER: Encourage the children to talk about the game. Replay the game in small groups. Ask: *Are different rings possible?* Ask the children to explain how they know which domino is hidden. Call out a number and ask the children to hold up the number of fingers needed to make a total of 6 with this number.

COIN FEEL
OBJECTIVES: To recognize coins of different values. To solve simple money problems. To add more than two numbers together.
BEFORE: Real coins **must** be used for this activity. Lay out various coins and remind the class of their values.
AFTER: Encourage the children to say which coins are easier to tell apart by feel. Talk about the coin values.

Play the game in pairs, with one child asking another to find a particular coin. Pass a coin around a group: each child has to say something different about it.

COIN RUB
OBJECTIVES: To recognize coins of different values. To add and subtract using coins. To add more than two numbers together.
BEFORE: Real coins **must** be used for this activity. Rub a coin for the group to identify. List the coins in use.
AFTER: Look at and discuss the children's rubbings. Display them for other children to match with coins. Discuss and compare heads and tails. Work out how much a rubbed-coin picture is worth (you might decide to restrict the range of coins used). Discuss easy ways of adding the coins.

MAKE 10P
OBJECTIVES: To add and subtract using money. To choose and use appropriate operations to solve a problem. To add more than two numbers together. To count on in steps of 2 and 10.
BEFORE: Play the game against the class. Demonstrate that a number of coins can be exchanged for one coin of the same total value.
AFTER: Encourage the children to talk about what happened and how they played the game. Replay the game and ask the children to explain their decisions. Ask: *What happens... if we play in threes? ...if you can add 1p, 2p or 3p when it is your turn?...if we include a 5p piece and play to 20p?* Try these out.

HIDDEN MONEY
OBJECTIVES: To choose and use appropriate operations and mental strategies to solve a simple problem involving money. To work out how to pay an exact sum using smaller coins.
BEFORE: Lay out a small number of 1p coins. Ask the children to close their eyes as you remove an amount, then look and tell you how much is hidden. Repeat this; but before they open their eyes, tell them how much is on the table. Can they work out the hidden amount? Remind them of the coin values. If necessary, play one game with mixed coins.
AFTER: Replay the game in small groups. Ask the children how they worked out the amounts. Try hiding a small amount and stating the total hidden, then asking the children **which coins** might be hidden.

MAKE A RECTANGLE
OBJECTIVES: To know that addition can be done in any order. To carry out addition by using known number facts and by counting on.
BEFORE: Demonstrate the activity by making a rectangle with playing cards and adding up the total together. Set the challenge: *What different totals can you make your rectangle worth?*
AFTER: Share the different totals achieved. What totals are possible? Talk about easy ways to add numbers.

MY NUMBER TRACK

YOU WILL NEED: A helper, some pens, the track on this sheet.

YOU ARE GOING TO: make your own **number track** to 30.

❏ Write a number on each space on the track, from 1 as far as you can go.

❏ Now find some numbers that are important for you. They might be your age, how many goldfish you have, your Gran's door number and so on. Colour the spaces of these special numbers, and write what they mean.

❏ Take your finished number track back to school.

BET YOU CAN'T

❏ Use your track to invent a dice game.

DEAR HELPER

THE POINT OF THIS ACTIVITY: is to give your child practice in counting, reading and writing numbers to 20 or 30. This activity will help your child to recognize numbers and to remember the position they hold in a line. Having a 'number line' like this in your head is important for doing mental arithmetic.

Remember that our counting system does not always sound the way it should! The 'teen' numbers are irregular and take some time to understand: they are said 'backwards', the units before the tens (*six-teen* instead of *ten-six*). Your child may also find it hard to distinguish between, for example, 13 and 30 or 14 and 40 when he or she hears these – try it!

YOU MIGHT LIKE TO:

● Ask for the track to be sent back home, and put it up where it will be seen every day. Refer to it whenever a number comes up in conversation – for example, birthdays and ages.

● Play a board game such as 'Snakes and Ladders', looking at the pattern of numbers on the board with your child. Count along it to 100.

IF YOU GET STUCK:

● Take every opportunity to encourage your child to count aloud. The more often he or she does this, the better he or she will remember the counting sequence. Make it a fun activity.

● Refer to a tape measure to help your child remember the order of the numbers.

● If your child has difficulty writing the numbers, ask him or her to tell you what to write and then write it yourself.

Please sign: . . . .

MENTAL MATHS HOMEWORK

COUNTING AND ORDERING

IMPACT

STAND UP, SIT DOWN

YOU WILL NEED: A helper, a seat each.

YOU ARE GOING TO: count on the move!

❑ Link arms with your helper. Stand up and say 'ONE', then sit down and say 'TWO', then stand up and say 'THREE'...

❑ Carry on sitting and standing and counting together until you need a rest – or get it wrong!

❑ Now start at 20 (sitting), stand and say '21' and count on up to 29 like this. (Will you be sitting or standing when you say 29?)

❑ Try the same thing counting **backwards** from 29 to 20. Then have a rest!

❑ Think of something else that you can do when you're counting instead of sitting and standing.

BET YOU CAN'T

❑ Count backwards from 29 to 0.

❑ Bounce a ball, clap or jump while counting to 30. When you get to 30, or you drop the ball, start from 1 again. At school, you will be playing a people-counting game in a big group.

DEAR HELPER

THE POINT OF THIS ACTIVITY: is to practise the counting sequence. This type of counting is about knowing 'What number comes next?' rather than 'How many have you got?' Help your child to learn the pattern of the counting words between one and thirty – for example, six, seven, eight... twenty-**six**, twenty-**seven**, twenty-**eight**...

Remember that our counting system does not always sound the way it should! The 'teen' numbers are irregular and take some time to understand: they are said 'backwards', the units before the tens (*six-teen* instead of *ten-six*). Your child may also find it hard to distinguish between, for example, 13 and 30 or 14 and 40 when he or she hears these – try it! Also, remember that counting backwards is harder to master than counting forwards, because we don't do it as often. Your child may need to practise this more.

Play as many times as you both wish. This is a 'little and often' activity: the more often your child counts, the better he or she will become at it. Offer encouragement: having confidence is important.

YOU MIGHT LIKE TO: Try the same standing/sitting game, but start from sitting. Discuss which numbers were 'sitting' numbers (the odd numbers) and which were 'standing' numbers (the even numbers).

(We haven't done much on this yet)

IF YOU GET STUCK: Try counting aloud with your child while standing. Walk around, counting each step. Start from different numbers (not just 1), and don't forget to count backwards.

Please sign: . . . .

OUT AND ABOUT NUMBERS

YOU WILL NEED: A helper, pencil and paper – and fine weather!

YOU ARE GOING TO: collect some numbers from outdoors.

❑ Where might you see numbers outdoors? Make a list of all the places you might see a number written.

❑ Arrange to go out and collect some numbers. You might need to go out more than once, or go to different places. Write down every number you see.

❑ Discuss your list of numbers with your helper. Which is the largest number in your collection? Which is the smallest? What are the numbers for?

❑ Take back to school all the numbers you collect. They might be used for a display called 'We're going on a number hunt'.

BET YOU CAN'T

Put your numbers in order, from the smallest to the largest.

> ### HANDY HINT!
> You could ask your family to collect numbers when they are out and about, too! Don't forget to ask them where they found the numbers.

DEAR HELPER

THE POINT OF THIS ACTIVITY: is to start to read a variety of numbers (including numbers with two digits), and to link numbers with some of their real-life uses. This activity often captures children's interest, and may increase the number of questions your child asks about numbers around him or her – so be patient!

YOU MIGHT LIKE TO: talk about why the numbers are there. Numbers are often used in everyday life to label things, rather than to say how many – for example, the number 76 bus doesn't mean that there are another 75 buses in front of it.

IF YOU GET STUCK: with finding numbers, think about car numbers, video recorders, clocks, telephones, egg boxes, crisp packets...

Please sign: . . . .

RACE TO 20

YOU WILL NEED: A helper, a 1–6 dice (with dots), a collection of 'counters' (buttons or small toys), the playing track on this sheet.

YOU ARE GOING TO: play a counting game.
❑ One of the lanes is for you and one is for your helper. Put all the 'counters' where you can both reach them.
❑ Take turns to roll the dice. If you roll any number except 6, you place that number of your counters on your track, one in each space, starting from 1 (for example, 1, 2, 3). Then your helper rolls and puts the right number of counters on his or her track. When it is your turn again, you carry on placing counters in the next spaces (for example, 4, 5, 6). BUT if you roll a 6, you miss your go!
❑ The first player to fill all the spaces to 20 wins.
❑ You will be playing more counting games this week at school.

BET YOU CAN'T
❑ Race back to 1, after you reach 20, by taking the counters off the track when you roll the dice.
❑ Play 'Race to 20' – but instead of filling the track, fill a margarine or yoghurt pot. You will have to decide how you will know when you have collected 20 counters.

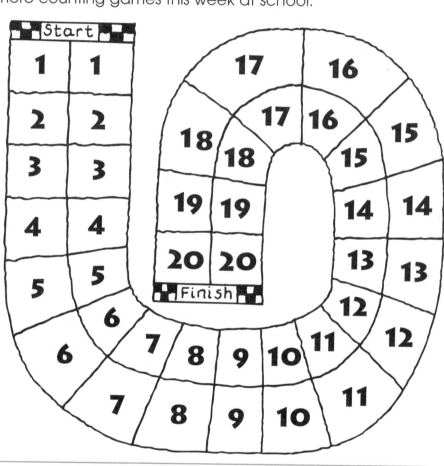

DEAR HELPER

THE POINT OF THIS ACTIVITY: is to practise counting a number of objects reliably. Help your child to count slowly, saying the number as he or she puts each counter on the track.

YOU MIGHT LIKE TO:
● Discuss how many counters you have after each turn. Your child may need to count them up instead of reading the number on the last space. If so, encourage him or her to touch the objects when counting them. Ask: *How many more do you need to win?*
● If your child is doing well, try playing with a dice with the numbers 1 to 6 instead of dots.

IF YOU GET STUCK: Try playing with a dice dotted 1, 2 and 3 (cover the 4 and 5 dots).

Please sign: . . . .

FILL IT

YOU WILL NEED: A helper; a small pot or box (such as a yoghurt pot or matchbox); a collection of little things (buttons, coins and so on); a pencil and paper.

YOU ARE GOING TO: estimate and then find out how many things fit inside your pot.

❑ Talk together about what things will fit inside your pot. For example, how many buttons do you think will fit? How many toy cars?

❑ Estimate (an **estimate** is a very good guess) how many of your objects will fit inside the pot, then find out by counting. How near were you?

❑ Try again, filling it with different objects.

❑ Ask your helper to write down what you find out. Take this information and your pot or box into school.

BET YOU CAN'T

❑ Find the largest number of things that will fit inside the pot!

❑ Fill your pot with different objects – maybe one pasta shape, one toy car, one coin, and so on. Make a list of what you were able to fit in and take this into school.

> I think this might hold 10 of my hair slides.

DEAR HELPER

THE POINT OF THIS ACTIVITY: is to practise estimating and counting accurately, and to compare quantities. Part of knowing about numbers is having a rough idea of what different quantities look like, and this skill develops through lots of experience of looking at things and being confident enough to make a **good guess**, without worrying about being completely accurate. Useful words to use are: **estimate, roughly, fewer, more, about the same, too few, too many**.

YOU MIGHT LIKE TO: Discuss what kind of objects would be suitable for filling the pot or box before you

start. When you empty it, make sure each object is touched and moved as it is counted.

IF YOU GET STUCK: Let your child change his or her first estimate. This will help him or her to become more confident about having a go in the first place. It might help to count out 10 objects together and keep these nearby as a reminder of what 10 'looks like'. Does your child think the container will hold more or fewer than 10 of these objects?

Please sign: . . . .

DOT-TO-DOT

YOU WILL NEED: A helper, a pencil, this sheet.

YOU ARE GOING TO: solve this dot-to-dot puzzle by reading and ordering some numbers.

❏ Start by counting together in ones from 1 to 30. Can you count backwards in ones from 30 down to 1?

❏ Talk to your helper about dot-to-dot puzzles.

❏ Look at this dot-to-dot puzzle. It doesn't start at 1. Find the smallest number. This is where you will start joining the dots.

❏ Now read and join all the numbers in order to the end. What picture did you make?

❏ Take your finished dot-to-dot sheets into school.

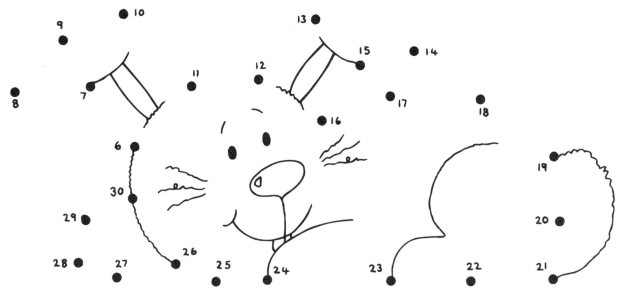

BET YOU CAN'T

Make your own dot-to-dot puzzle by tracing the dots on this puzzle (don't draw the lines or write the numbers). Now choose a number to start at and write it on the first dot, write the next number on the next dot, and so on to the end.

DEAR HELPER

THE POINT OF THIS ACTIVITY: is to practise reading and ordering numbers under 30. It is important to see the numbers in order (as well as hear them) when we count, because the pattern of our counting sequence does not sound as it should! The 'teen' numbers are hard because they are said 'backwards', with the units before the tens (*six-teen* instead of *ten-six*). Your child may also confuse 13 with 30, 14 with 40 and so on when he or she hears these spoken.

YOU MIGHT LIKE TO: Write all the numbers in this dot-to-dot puzzle as a list. Cover one of the numbers

with your finger, then ask your child to tell you which number is covered.

IF YOU GET STUCK:
● Try re-numbering the dots from 1 to 20.
● Practise counting aloud together to 20, and later to 30, but starting from different numbers. Ask: *Where shall we start counting from today?* Practise counting backwards too.

Please sign: . . . .

LADDERS

YOU WILL NEED: A helper, a pack of playing cards, this sheet, a pencil.

YOU ARE GOING TO: play a game by putting the numbers 1 to 10 in order.

❑ START by sorting out **one** black suit (Clubs or Spades) and **one** red suit (Hearts or Diamonds) from the pack. Now take out all the picture cards (Kings, Queens, and Jacks). You won't need these.

❑ Decide who is having the red suit and who is having the black suit. Shuffle your own suit and put the cards in a pile, face down.

RULES

❑ Turn over a card. What number does it show? Can you write this in the right place (for example, 6 in the sixth space) on your ladder?

❑ Now it is your helper's turn to turn over a card and write that number on his or her ladder.

❑ Carry on taking turns. If you turn over a number you have already written on your ladder, you miss that go!

❑ Who fills a ladder first?

❑ Play again.

❑ Take your filled-in ladders into school.

BET YOU CAN'T

Draw two ladders with 20 rungs each, and play the game with a set of cards to 20.

DEAR HELPER

THE POINT OF THIS ACTIVITY: is to practise ordering a set of numbers by finding their positions on a number track. Your child will also be practising reading and writing numbers. Be patient and allow your child to find the number's position without help.

YOU MIGHT LIKE TO:
● Play a number of times and talk about what happens.
● Ask your child, when the ladder is full, to shut his or her eyes while you cover one of the numbers -- and

then to open his or her eyes and work out which number is covered.

IF YOU GET STUCK: Show your child how to work out where each number belongs on the ladder. If he or she is having trouble writing the numbers, ask him or her to tell you where to write them. Writing numbers is a handwriting skill; your child may lack this skill, but still be able to do the maths!

Please sign: . . . .

COUNTING AND ORDERING

IMPACT

MENTAL MATHS HOMEWORK

RACE THE NUMBERS

YOU WILL NEED: A helper, the 'Race the numbers' track on page 17, a pencil, a dice (with dots), a pack of playing cards with the picture cards (Kings, Queens and Jacks) taken out.

YOU ARE GOING TO: play a game where you write and 'race' numbers.

RULES

❑ Take turns to roll the dice and turn over a card. Which number is larger: the dice number or the card number?

❑ Write the **larger** number in the right row on the sheet – all the 2s go in the '2' row, all the 3s in the '3' row, and so on.

❑ Your partner now rolls the dice and turns over another card, then writes the larger number in the right row as before.

❑ Carry on like this until one number reaches the end. Which number wins?

❑ What do you notice about this game? Play again and see if the same things happen.

❑ Take your finished race sheet back to school. Talk to your friends – what happened when they played it?

BET YOU CAN'T

Play using a dice with numbers instead of dots.

Finish

1	I	I					
2	2	2	2				
3	3	3					
4	4						
5	5	5					
6	6	6					
7							
8	8						
9							
10							

DEAR HELPER

THE POINT OF THIS ACTIVITY: is to help your child to order numbers without starting at 1 and counting through each time. He or she will also be practising reading and writing numbers.

YOU MIGHT LIKE TO: Talk about which numbers are more likely to come up and which are not.

IF YOU GET STUCK:
● Try writing the smaller number instead of the larger, as this will mean that you only have to write numbers to 6.
● Alternatively, you could play with two dice and help your child to compare the numbers of dots on the dice.
● If your child has trouble writing the numbers, write them yourself. Writing numbers is a handwriting skill; if your child tells you where to write the number, he or she is still doing the maths!

Please sign: . . . .

COUNTING AND ORDERING

IMPACT

'RACE THE NUMBERS' TRACK

Finish

1						
2						
3						
4						
5						
6						
7						
8						
9						
10						

SHAKE, GUESS AND COUNT

YOU WILL NEED: A helper, a pot with a lid, at least 20 small things (coins, buttons or dried pasta).

YOU ARE GOING TO: do some estimating and counting.

❑ Secretly count some buttons into your pot. Remember how many you have put inside.

❑ Put on the lid and shake the pot gently. Ask your helper how many buttons he or she thinks are inside. Tip them out and count them.

❑ Now let your helper secretly put some buttons in the pot. Guess how many there are.

❑ Play again.

❑ Take your pot, with your counters inside, back to school to help make a number display.

BET YOU CAN'T
Try with several different-sized things in the pot – does it make a difference?

DEAR HELPER

THE POINT OF THIS ACTIVITY: is to reinforce your child's ability to count reliably, and to encourage him or her to make sensible estimates of small quantities (based on hearing and not seeing).

YOU MIGHT LIKE TO: Discuss how many counters could be inside, using mathematical vocabulary such as **estimate, roughly, fewer, more, about the same as, too few, too many.**

IF YOU GET STUCK:
● To estimate well requires both experience and confidence. Enjoy the estimating: it doesn't matter at this stage if your child suggests a crazy amount. Try making a 'silly estimate' and a 'serious estimate'.
● Help your child to count accurately by encouraging him or her to touch and move each object.

Please sign: . . . .

COUNTING AND ORDERING

IMPACT

TEENY MONEY

YOU WILL NEED: A helper, some 10p and 1p coins, a pencil and paper.

YOU ARE GOING TO: practise counting on and taking away from 10p.

❑ Lay down one 10p coin and line up some 1p coins next to it. How much money is in the line? Count on aloud from 10p, like this:

10,11,12,13p!

❑ Take the 10p away. How much do you have now?

❑ Make a new row of pennies with one 10p. Count up how much there is. If you take away the 10p, how much do you have left?

❑ Make a third row. How much money do you have with the 10p? How much without?

❑ Draw around the coins on a piece of paper. Write the amounts next to each row you make. Take the paper into school.

BET YOU CAN'T

Use the row of coins to help you count backwards from 19 to 10.

DEAR HELPER

THE POINT OF THIS ACTIVITY: is for your child to look at how numbers from 10 to 20 are made up with a ten and some ones, and to begin to know 10 more or 10 less without counting. This activity also helps your child to practise **counting on** from 10. To **count on**, you need to 'hold 10 in your head' and say the next number: 10, 11, 12, 13... Some children need a lot of practice to count on from numbers other than 1.

YOU MIGHT LIKE TO:
● Take away the 10p and ask your child whether he or she needs to count the remaining 1p coins or know how many are left. Say: *14 take away 10 leaves 4 and 15 take away 10 leaves 5. So what do you think 16 take away 10 leaves? Prove it!*

● Practise counting backwards through the 'teen' numbers.

IF YOU GET STUCK:
● Look at the row of coins and ask your child to use his or her hands and feet to show you how much money is there – stretching out both feet for 10 and using individual fingers for the ones.

● Provide practice in counting on. Lay out a row of 1p coins, then cover the first two. Say the number covered like this: *Twooo*. Now count on to the end of the row, touching each coin as you count: *three* (touch), *four* (touch)...

Please sign: . . . .

COUNTING AND ORDERING

IMPACT

ADD 10 OR ADD 1

YOU WILL NEED: A helper, a pack of playing cards with all the picture cards (Kings, Queens, Jacks) removed, a pencil and paper.

YOU ARE GOING TO: practise adding 10 or 1 as quickly as you can.
❑ Start by sorting out your pack of cards. You need all the tens and ones (Aces) in one pile. This is the ADD pile. Put all the other cards in another pile. This is the NUMBER pile. Place each pile face down.

❑ One of you (the number-person) turns over a card from the number pile and calls out the number on it. The other player (the add-person) turns over a card from the add pile. If it is a 10, the add-person calls out 'Add 10'. If it is an Ace (1), he or she calls out 'Add 1'.
❑ The number-person has to say the answer as quickly as possible.
❑ Carry on to the end of the pack, then swap piles and play again.

❑ Did you get any quicker at adding 10 and adding 1? Ask your helper to write down your ideas. Back at school, be ready to talk about what you found hard and what you found easier.

Add 10.

BET YOU CAN'T
Add the picture cards (Kings, Queens, Jacks) to the add pile. If you pick up a picture card, you can choose to call out **either** 'Add 10' **or** 'Add 1'.

DEAR HELPER

THE POINT OF THIS ACTIVITY: is to help your child know by heart the number that is 1 or 10 more than any number to 10, without counting. This will help him or her to calculate mentally.

YOU MIGHT LIKE TO:
● Start with you as the number-person and your child as the add-person. Talk to your child about how you are adding the 10s.
● Look at the '10-jumps' on a **number line** (a line of numbers in order, stretching from 0 or below to 100 or

above). A tape-measure works well as a home-made number line.

IF YOU GET STUCK: Take out the 10-cards and just practise adding and subtracting 1, using the black Aces for 'add 1' and the red Aces for 'subtract 1'. (You may need to borrow more Aces from a second pack of cards.)

Please sign: . . . .

ORDER AND CHANGE

YOU WILL NEED: A helper, a pack of playing cards, lots of counters (buttons, pasta shapes or other things), a timer, a blank piece of card, scissors, a marker pen or crayon, a pencil and paper.

YOU ARE GOING TO: put numbers in order and play a hiding game.
❏ Start by choosing one suit (Hearts, Diamonds, Spades or Clubs). Take out all the picture cards (Kings, Queens, Jacks) – you will not need these.
❏ Now make an extra card (from a blank piece of card). Mark it '0' for zero with a marker pen or crayon.

PART 1: Shuffle your suit of cards and spread them out on the table, face up. Then, as quickly as you can, put all the cards in order from zero to 10.
❏ Try again and see if you can do it more quickly. Make a note of your best time.

PART 2: Now put the right number of 'counters' below each card: four counters below the 4-card and so on.

PART 3: Ask your helper to close his or her eyes while you make a small change to your line of numbers. You might turn over one card to make a 'missing number', take away a counter, add a counter, or even move a counter from one number to another.
❏ Ask your helper to open his or her eyes and tell you EXACTLY what has changed.
❏ Put the line back as it was and swap roles.
❏ Back at school, be ready to play more ordering games.

YOU MIGHT LIKE TO TRY
Ordering the cards backwards, from 10 to 0, as quickly as you can.

> **HANDY HINT!**
> Put your 'counters' in a pattern, so it is easy to see how many there are!

DEAR HELPER

THE POINT OF THIS ACTIVITY: is to help your child become more familiar with the sequence of numbers. Playing the game with the counters will give him or her experience of the value of numbers, and practice in scanning a display and recognizing a number of objects without counting every one.

YOU MIGHT LIKE TO:
● Discuss how arranging counters in patterns helps you to spot how many there are. Most people find it difficult to recognize amounts above 4 unless they form a familiar pattern, such as the dots on a dice.

● Use a different set of numbers, perhaps 15 to 25, once you feel that your child is sure of ordering numbers to 10.

IF YOU GET STUCK:
● Try ordering numbers to 5.
● Practise recognizing small numbers in patterns by laying out a few items, concealing them and letting your child 'peep' at the pattern.

Please sign: . . . .

FOLLOW ON

YOU WILL NEED: A helper, a pack of playing cards, a pencil and paper.

YOU ARE GOING TO: play a game by putting numbers in order.

❑ Take out all the picture cards (Kings, Queens and Jacks). You will not need these.

❑ Now find all the Ace cards and put them face up on the table. Each of these is a 1.

❑ Shuffle the other cards and deal out five cards each. Put the cards that are left in a pile, face down.

RULES

❑ Look at the Aces on the table, then look at your hand. Do you have any of the cards that follow the ones on the table? A 2 of Hearts will follow an Ace of Hearts, a 2 of Clubs will follow an Ace of Clubs, and so on.

❑ If you have a 2 in the right suit, lay it on its Ace. If not, pick up a card from the face down pile.

❑ Now your helper looks at his or her cards and finds a card to follow on from the cards on the table. So a 2 could follow on from an Ace, or a 3 could follow on from a 2.

❑ Carry on taking turns like this until all the cards are in order on the table.

❑ Make a list of your playing cards in order. Take this into school. You will be playing more ordering games there.

BET YOU CAN'T

❑ Start with all the 5s on the table. When it is your turn, you can find cards to follow on either above or below (so 5 could have either a 6 in front or a 4 behind).

┌ **DEAR HELPER** ───────────────────────

THE POINT OF THIS ACTIVITY: is to help your child become more familiar with the sequence of numbers. He or she will have to scan a hand of cards to find one that fits in one of the incomplete sequences.

YOU MIGHT LIKE TO: use the completed sequence to ask your child some questions, such as *Which number is between 3 and 5?* and *Which number is 1 less than 9?* Can your child answer these questions

with eyes shut, only opening them to check? Useful words and phrases to use are: **first, next, last, before, after, between, smaller, larger, 1 more, 1 less, 2 more, 2 less...**

IF YOU GET STUCK: try playing with just one or two suits, or with all four suits but only up to 5.

Please sign: . . . .

WRITE IT IN

YOU WILL NEED: A helper, some coloured pencils or crayons, this grid.

YOU ARE GOING TO: make a number grid by counting to 25, then talk about the patterns you find.

❏ Start at 1 and count along the top row of the grid. What number belongs in the **last** square on the top row? Write it in.

❏ Put your finger in the square underneath the 1. Write in 6. Carry on counting along this row. Which number belongs in the **last** square? Write it in.

❏ Carry on writing in the first and last numbers in each row until you reach the end of the grid.

❏ Talk about what you notice. Try to explain it to your helper.

1				

❏ Now write in all the missing numbers, one at a time, by counting along from 1.
Talk about the patterns you find.
Colour one in on your grid.

❏ Try reading out these numbers forwards to 25 and then backwards from 25 down to 1.

❏ Take your finished number grid back to school and talk about it.

YOU MIGHT LIKE TO TRY

❏ Letting your helper cover one of the numbers on the grid. Can you tell which one is hidden?

❏ Writing in the numbers to 24 on some different-shaped grids.

DEAR HELPER

THE POINT OF THIS ACTIVITY: is to look for and talk about patterns in the counting sequence to 25. Recognizing a number pattern and using it to predict a coming number is an important mathematical skill. Encourage your child to practise counting both forwards and backwards. Your child will also be practising writing the numbers (check that he or she gets them the right way round).

YOU MIGHT LIKE TO:
● Encourage your child to predict which number comes next. Be patient while he or she tries to explain

the patterns – your child may not see the same patterns as you, and this is OK.
● Hide a number on the completed grid for your child to name (see above), then ask your child to explain how he or she knew which number it was.

IF YOU GET STUCK: Try writing the numbers yourself – but encourage your child to tell you what number to write and where to write it. It is important for your child to hear you counting both forwards and backwards.

Please sign: . . . .

ADDITION AND SUBTRACTION

TAKE ME AWAY

YOU WILL NEED: A helper; this sheet; 20 small counters such as buttons, a special dice that has the numbers 1, 2, 3, 1, 2, 3 (you could use a normal dotted dice or a cube building-block and put on stickers with the numbers).

YOU ARE GOING TO: do some counting and some taking away (subtraction).
❑ Decide which line of squares is yours and which is for your helper.
❑ Put one counter on each of your squares. Check how many there are.

TO PLAY:
❑ Roll the dice and look at the number. **Take away** that number of counters from your line. How many counters are left?
❑ Now it is your helper's turn to roll the dice.
❑ Each time, tell each other how many counters you start with, how many you take away and how many are left.
❑ The first player to empty his or her line is the winner – but you have to roll the exact number to finish. For example, if you have one counter left, you must roll a 1: a 2 or a 3 won't do.
❑ Back at school, you will be talking about subtraction. Take in your counters in a bag to play with.

BET YOU CAN'T
❑ Start filling your line again when it is empty, by rolling the dice and **adding** that number of counters.
❑ Play with a longer line of squares.

DEAR HELPER

THE POINT OF THIS ACTIVITY: is to help your child to understand **subtraction** (or 'taking away'). This game will help your child to see that we end up with fewer counters each time we subtract. While playing, your child will also be practising using the correct language to say what is happening.

YOU MIGHT LIKE TO:
● Help your child to use the correct mathematical language by talking about what is happening. Use words and phrases such as: **take, take from, one fewer, two fewer, three fewer, leaves, left.**

● Encourage your child to predict what might happen by asking *What number do you need to roll now?*
● Notice what numbers he or she can recognize instantly without having to count them up.

IF YOU GET STUCK: Play with a dice that has dots to 3 instead of numbers. Be patient while your child learns to count the dots and remove the right amount from the line. Count the dots and counters together.

Please sign: . . . .

IMPACT

EGG BOXES

YOU WILL NEED: A helper, a dotted dice, at least two egg boxes each, some small things (to be 'eggs').

YOU ARE GOING TO: add 'eggs' to your boxes to make up sets of 6.
❑ Share out the empty egg boxes.
❑ Take turns to roll the dice. The number tells you how many 'eggs' you can put in your box. But if you roll a 6, you miss a go.
❑ When you have filled a box, put any leftover 'eggs' from that turn in the next box. Then carry on.
❑ After each turn, answer these questions:
• *How many eggs are in this box?*
• *How many more eggs do you need to fill it?*
❑ When one of you has filled all his or her egg boxes, stop. How many 'eggs' do each of you have?

❑ Take your egg boxes back to school, where you will be playing another egg box adding game.

Now my egg box is full!

BET YOU CAN'T
❑ Play with some 12-boxes, or even some 18-boxes!
❑ Introduce another rule – maybe this: *If you can say how many more you need to make 6, you can have an extra go.*

DEAR HELPER

THE POINT OF THIS ACTIVITY: is to help your child understand **addition**. The game focuses on adding numbers to make 6. While playing, your child will also be practising using the correct language to explain what is happening.

YOU MIGHT LIKE TO:
● Help your child to use the correct mathematical language by talking about what is happening. Use words and phrases such as: **one more, two more, total, add, how many more, altogether.**

● Encourage your child to predict what might happen by asking *What number do you need to roll now?*
● Notice which numbers your child can recognize instantly without having to count the objects (or spaces).

IF YOU GET STUCK: Practise adding up to 4 by cutting the egg-boxes so that they only have four spaces, and using a dice marked 1, 2, 3, 1, 2, 3.

Please sign: . . . .

ADDITION AND SUBTRACTION

IMPACT

TWO-COUNTER RACE

YOU WILL NEED: A helper, a pack of playing cards, the 'Racing tracks' on page 47, a little red 'counter' and a little black 'counter' each.

YOU ARE GOING TO: play a game that involves adding two numbers in any order.

❑ Take out all the cards over 5. You won't need these. The Aces count as 1.

❑ Put all the **red 1–5 cards** together, shuffle them and put them face down in a pile. Do the same to make a **black 1–5 card** pile.

❑ Choose a track each. Put both of your counters on the Start of your track.

❑ Turn over one red card and one black card. Add the two card numbers together. This tells you how far you can move your two counters along the track.

❑ Move your BLACK counter the number on the BLACK card first, and then add on the red number. Where do you end up?

❑ Now move your RED counter the number on the RED card first, and then add on the black number.

❑ Do you end up in the same place both times? Explain to your helper why this happens.

❑ Take turns to turn over the two cards and move the two counters forwards as above. The first player to reach the end of the track wins.

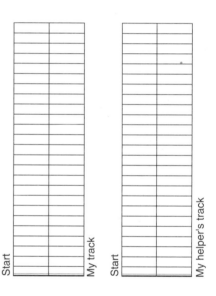

❑ Write down some of the different pairs of numbers you moved your counters, or ask your helper to write them down for you. Take your numbers into school.

BET YOU CAN'T

Race back again from the end of the track.

DEAR HELPER

THE POINT OF THIS ACTIVITY: is for your child to recognize that numbers can be added together in any order. Whether you add 3 to 2 or 2 to 3, you still get 5. Your child will also be practising addition involving numbers to 10.

YOU MIGHT LIKE TO:
● Encourage your child to hold the first number in his or her head and **count on** the second number: '4 add 3, that's FOUR... 5, 6, 7'.
● Ask your child to look at the cards that have been

turned over each time and predict where the counters will end up.

IF YOU GET STUCK:
● Turn over one card at a time, so that your child has to count the black number first and then add the red number on to that.
● You could try using 1–3 cards only, so that your child can practise addition involving numbers to 6.

Please sign: . . . .

ADDITION AND SUBTRACTION

IMPACT

FINGERS FIVE

YOU WILL NEED: Your hands, your helper's hands, a pencil and paper.

YOU ARE GOING TO: use your fingers to look at how numbers from 6 to 10 can be broken into 5 and a bit.

❑ Both of you hold up 7 fingers. Look at how you both made the 7. Is it 5 and 2? Or is it 3 and 4? Can you show 7 a different way? (6 and 1 is tricky using your hands!)

❑ Next, find different ways of holding up 8 fingers. Call these out. Try with 9 fingers.

Now you are ready to play **Fingers Five**, like this:

❑ You hold up 5 fingers (one hand). Your helper has to hold up some more fingers to add onto the 5. Both of you call out: '5 and 2 more make 7'.

❑ Swap round, with your helper holding up the 5 and you holding up the extra fingers.

❑ Play again a few times.

❑ Draw your hands showing a number as 5 and a bit, or write down the numbers you made and how you made them. Take your paper into school.

BET YOU CAN'T

❑ Recognize the number straight away without counting the fingers.

❑ Play **Fingers Ten**. You hold up two hands to show 10, and your helper holds up some single fingers. You then say how many fingers that makes altogether: 'That's 10 and 2 more – TEN, 11, 12.'

DEAR HELPER

THE POINT OF THIS ACTIVITY: is to see how numbers from 6 to 10 can be broken into '5 and something'. Hands are particularly good for showing this. Your child will also be practising addition involving numbers up to 10, and experiencing **counting on**. Counting on means being able to hold a number in your head and count on in 1s from there: 'FIVE... 6, 7'.

YOU MIGHT LIKE TO: Encourage your child to say the amount without counting. Let him or her take a 'peep' at your hand, then cover it with a handkerchief. Allow as many 'peeps' as are needed!

IF YOU GET STUCK: Try to remember that some children find counting on very difficult to master. If your child resorts to counting all the fingers even when he or she must know that the first hand shows 5 fingers, be encouraging. Give him or her lots of practice at 'holding the number in your head' and counting on from there. Try holding up 5, chanting 'FIVE!' together, taking that hand away and then counting on some single fingers on the other hand together.

Please sign: . . . .

FIND THE TENS

YOU WILL NEED: A helper, two packs of playing cards with the tens and the picture cards (Jacks, Queens and Kings) taken out, a pencil and paper.

YOU ARE GOING TO: make a pattern with the pairs of numbers that total 10.
❑ Find all the Heart cards and spread them out on a table, face up. With your helper, pick up one Heart card and look for its partner card to total 10. Aces count as 1. So if you pick up a 9, you will search for an Ace.
❑ Carry on matching pairs.
❑ Now lay all the Heart pairs in order, from 1 and 9 up to... 9 and 1! Talk about the patterns you notice.
❑ Order all the other suit pairs in the same way, one suit at a time.
❑ Try to write down or draw your addition pattern. Take it into school.

BET YOU CAN'T
Play a 'Snap' game where you have to be quick to spot the card that goes with the one you are holding to total 10.

DEAR HELPER

THE POINT OF THIS ACTIVITY: is to practise finding the pairs of numbers that total 10. Your child is working towards knowing these pairs by heart. Recognizing patterns in addition and subtraction, and being able to use them to work something out, is a very useful mental calculation skill.

YOU MIGHT LIKE TO: Try turning over a card while your child closes his or her eyes, and asking him or her to work out the hidden number by looking at the pattern. Can your child explain how he or she knows the number?

IF YOU GET STUCK: Take out all the cards above 5, and work on finding and ordering pairs that total 5.

Please sign: . . . .

ADD THEM ALL UP

YOU WILL NEED: A helper, a pack of playing cards with all the cards over 5 taken out, a small counter each, the racing track on page 47, a pencil and paper.

YOU ARE GOING TO: practise adding three numbers together by using number-pairs that you already know.

❏ Shuffle the pack of cards. Decide who will start. Put your counter on the 'Start' line of your track.

❏ If you are starting, turn over the **top three cards**. What numbers do you have?

❏ Look for two cards with numbers that you can add up straight away. Hold this total in your head and add on the number on the last card. Put the three cards on one side.

❏ What is your total? Move your counter forward this number of spaces on the top track.

❏ Now it is your helper's turn to do the same thing.

❏ Carry on moving your counters along the top track, and then back along the bottom track until you run out of cards. Whoever's counter is in front wins.

❏ Back at school, you will be adding some more numbers and talking about the number-pairs that you know straight away. Write these down and take them into school.

BET YOU CAN'T

Play until someone reaches the 'Start' line again. This person is the winner. If you want to do this, you will have to put your three cards back under the pack when you have used them.

DEAR HELPER

THE POINT OF THIS ACTIVITY: is to practise adding more than two numbers together by recognizing and using additions that your child already knows by heart. For example, if your child knows that 2 and 3 make 5, he or she will need to recognize this pair among other numbers **and** hold the total in his or her head before adding on the third number. This is quite a complicated skill!

YOU MIGHT LIKE TO:
● Use mathematical vocabulary for addition, such as **add, more, plus, makes, total, altogether** and **how many more.**

● Notice any additions that your child knows by heart.

IF YOU GET STUCK:
● Remember that this game uses a combination of skills, so your child will need lots of encouragement. Be patient and help him or her to sort out the three cards and find two that are easy to add. Say this total out loud, so that your child can count on from it.
● Turn over three cards, look for a pair you can add easily and move just that number of spaces along the track.

Please sign: . . . .

FIND THE DIFFERENCE

YOU WILL NEED: A helper, a pack of playing cards with all the cards over 5 taken out, a counter each, the 'Racing tracks' on page 47.

YOU ARE GOING TO: play a game that helps you to practise subtraction.

❏ Shuffle the pack of cards. Decide who will start. Put your counter on the 'Start' line of your track.

❏ If you are starting, turn over the **top two cards**. What numbers do you have?

❏ Find the **difference** between them. (You may need to tell your helper what 'the difference' means.)

❏ Tell your helper what the difference between your two numbers is, and how you worked it out. Move your counter that number of spaces on the board, then put the two cards on one side.

❏ Now it is your helper's turn to do the same thing.

❏ Carry on moving your counter along the top track, then back along the  bottom track until you run out of cards. Whose counter is in front?

❏ Back at school, you will be subtracting some more numbers and talking about the differences you know straight away. Write these down and take them into school.

BET YOU CAN'T

Play until someone reaches the start line again. This person is the LOSER! If you want to do this, you will have to put your two cards back under the pack when you have used them.

DEAR HELPER

THE POINT OF THIS ACTIVITY: is to practise subtracting one number from another. Your child is working towards learning by heart the subtraction facts for all numbers up to 10 (for example, '7 take away 4 leaves 3'). To know these facts, he or she needs to practise them; this game should be an enjoyable way to do that.

Finding the difference between two numbers means looking at them and working out how much larger the larger number is than the smaller number. For example, the difference between 5 and 3 is 2. Encourage your child to explain how he or she works out the difference between two numbers. It might be by counting on from

3 to 5, or just by 'knowing' that 5 is two more than 3.

YOU MIGHT LIKE TO: Use mathematical vocabulary for subtraction, such as **take, take away, subtract, difference between, leaves**. Notice any subtractions that your child already knows by heart.

IF YOU GET STUCK: Spread out the cards face up. Encourage your child to choose two numbers and subtract one from the other. Move this number of spaces along the track.

Please sign: . . . .

ADDITION AND SUBTRACTION

IMPACT

CALENDAR COUNTDOWN

YOU WILL NEED: A helper, some sticky labels, a pencil, a container and some counters (such as buttons or pasta shapes) to fit inside it. A see-through container is best!

YOU ARE GOING TO: make a Countdown Calendar.

❑ Talk to your helper about anything special that is going to happen during the next few weeks. You might be meeting a friend, or be going on holiday, or it might even be your birthday!

❑ Write something that you are looking forward to on a label, then stick it onto your container. Together, put one 'counter' into the container for each day that is left until THE BIG DAY! Don't forget today's counter.

❑ This is your Countdown Calendar. How many days do you have until THE BIG DAY?

❑ Now start counting down to that day. When each day has passed, take out one counter. This will help you to keep track of how many days are left.

❑ Put each counter that you take away into a second container. This will help you to see how many days have passed.

HANDY HINT!
Count your counters regularly!

The cup Final match

❑ Back at school, you will be talking about your calendars and making a class calendar. When your BIG DAY arrives, write down the date and what is happening. Take your writing back to school.

BET YOU CAN'T

Tell your helper what has happened to the numbers of counters, like this: 'There were 10 buttons in the pot. Now that we have taken out 7, there are only 3 left.'

DEAR HELPER

THE POINT OF THIS ACTIVITY: is to show your child a simple way of marking the passage of time. Time is a difficult concept, and many young children have trouble thinking of 'days' as fixed amounts of time. The counters allow them to count the days left and the days that have already passed.

This is also a simple subtraction activity which emphasizes that subtracting makes an amount smaller, and that it 'undoes' addition (for example: *There were 10 buttons in the pot, and now that we have taken out 7 there are only 3 left*). It also provides an opportunity to count and compare amounts: *There were 7 in there yesterday, and now there are only 6.*

YOU MIGHT LIKE TO:
● Use the mathematical vocabulary of subtraction (for example, **one fewer, three fewer, leaves, how many left, take, take away**) when discussing the counters and the passing days.
● Relate the counters in the container to the day-spaces on a calendar.

IF YOU GET STUCK: You have probably chosen an event that is too far off! This activity should be relatively trouble-free.

Please sign: . . . .

DOMINO DOUBLES

YOU WILL NEED: A helper, a box of dominoes, a pencil and paper.

YOU ARE GOING TO: look for double and near-double numbers.

❑ Spread out the dominoes and find all the **doubles** – that is, the dominoes that look like this:

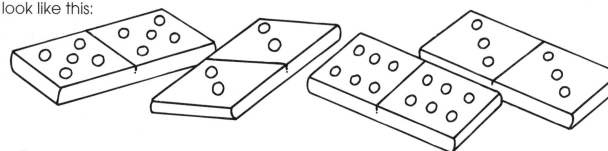

❑ Do you know the **totals** of any of these doubles? For example: double 5 is 10 (there are 10 spots on a double-5 domino).

❑ Lay all the doubles in order.

❑ Can you and your helper work out the totals of all these doubles?

❑ Now find some **near-doubles**. A near-double is very close to a double – for example:

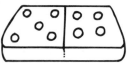 is nearly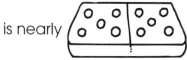

❑ Pair off each double with a near-double. Look at the spots and explain what you see.

❑ Draw or write down your pairs of doubles and near-doubles. Take your paper into school.

BET YOU CAN'T

Work out how many spots there are on the near-doubles by looking at the doubles – WITHOUT COUNTING the spots on ANY domino!

DEAR HELPER

THE POINT OF THIS ACTIVITY: is to practise doubling small numbers (a useful mental arithmetic skill), and to identify totals that can be figured out from those your child already knows. Mathematics will seem very tiresome to children who think they have to remember everything! In reality, we need to be able to remember some things and use this knowledge to figure out the things we don't know.

YOU MIGHT LIKE TO: Build your child's confidence by congratulating him or her on what he or she notices. The important thing is that your child **does not resort to counting the spots.** Saying aloud the numbers on the

domino ends will help your child to focus on these numbers.

IF YOU GET STUCK: Only use dominoes up to double 3 or double 4. The important thing is that your child **does not resort to counting the spots.** Allow him or her to take a 'peep' at the domino end, then cover it. Allow more peeps if necessary. Keep the numbers small enough for your child to concentrate on the relationships between them – for example, *The 5 has got one more spot than the 4.*

Please sign: . . . .

ADDITION AND SUBTRACTION

IMPACT

NO TENS ALLOWED

YOU WILL NEED: A helper; all the Aces, 2s and 3s from two packs of playing cards.

YOU ARE GOING TO: practise adding numbers together to make 10.

❑ Shuffle your cards. Lay the top card face up on the table.

❑ Deal out all the rest of the cards (more than two people can play). Spread all your cards in front of you, so that you can see them.

❑ Decide who will start. If it is you, then choose one of your cards to put alongside the card that is face up. The aim is to make a total of **any number except 10**. Aces count as 1.

❑ What do the numbers on these two cards make if you add them? If it's 10, you've lost! (That shouldn't happen in the first round.)

❑ Now it is your helper's turn. He or she must choose a card to lay alongside the two face-up cards, then add all three cards to make any total **except 10**.

❑ Go on playing like this until one of you makes 10 (the game is over), or until you run out of cards. If you go over 10, leave the last card, put the others on one side and carry on playing.

❑ Back at school you will be adding lots of numbers like this. Be ready to talk about easy ways of adding up.

BET YOU CAN'T
Play the game with your cards hidden from each other.

DEAR HELPER

THE POINT OF THIS ACTIVITY: is to practise adding more than two numbers together. Your child will have to do a lot of mental arithmetic to avoid making a total of 10. He or she should be thinking like this: *If I put the 3 it's OK, because 3, 2 and 3 together only make 8.*

YOU MIGHT LIKE TO: Discuss how you decide which cards to play. As you play this game with everyone's cards in full view this allows you to discuss different cards, and why you might play them. You will need to play more than once for your child to begin to think

about a winning strategy – *I will put the Ace because it will last longer.*

IF YOU GET STUCK: Your child may find it difficult to add more than two numbers (even small numbers) together. If so, encourage him or her to talk it through: *2 and 1 is 3, and 2 more makes...* A useful strategy is to look at the largest number first, hold it in your head and count on from there using fingers.

Please sign: . . . .

ADDITION AND SUBTRACTION

IMPACT

FLIP AND MOVE

YOU WILL NEED: A helper, a coin, the snake track on this page, a small toy each (to use as a counter).

YOU ARE GOING TO: play a game where you **predict** which number you will move to.

❑ Play this game with your helper. Put your 'counters' on the snake's tongue.

❑ To move to the end of the snake, take turns to flip the coin. If it lands on Heads, you move on 2 spaces. If it lands on Tails, you move on 1 space.

  BUT! You must say which number you will land on **before** you move!

❑ Decorate your snake track and take it back to school. You will be using it to play more games.

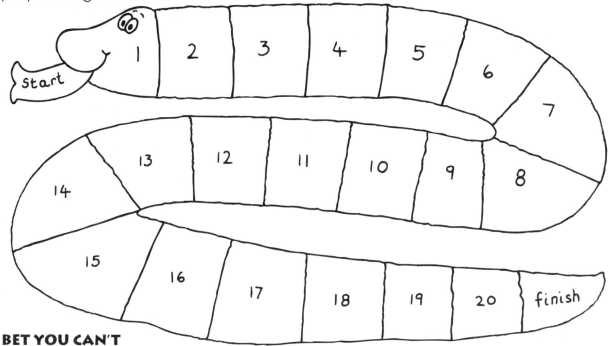

BET YOU CAN'T

❑ Race back again from the end of the track by **subtracting 2** for Heads and **taking away 1** for Tails. Again, you must say what number you will land on **before** you move!

DEAR HELPER

THE POINT OF THIS ACTIVITY: is to reinforce your child's understanding of addition and subtraction. He or she will be practising saying the number that is 1 more (or 1 less), or 2 more (or 2 less), than any number up to 20. Remind your child to **predict** the number that he or she will land on **before** touching the counter, by looking at the number that the counter is on.

YOU MIGHT LIKE TO: Help your child to use the correct mathematical language by talking about what is happening in the game, using words and phrases

such as **one more, two more, how many more, altogether, total, add, one fewer, two fewer, how many left, leaves, take, take away** and **subtract.**

IF YOU GET STUCK:
● Try racing to 10 instead of 20, then racing back again.
● It might help to stick a '2' label on one side of the coin and a '1' label on the other side.

Please sign: . . . .

FAIR TOWERS

YOU WILL NEED: A helper, a pack of playing cards with the picture cards (Jacks, Queens and Kings) taken out, a pile of Lego or similar bricks (it is important that all the bricks are the same size), a pencil and paper.

YOU ARE GOING TO: share some amounts **fairly** between the two of you.
❑ Shuffle the cards and put them in a pile, face down.
❑ Turn over the top card and count out that number of bricks. (Aces count as 1.)
❑ Use all of these bricks to make two towers, one for each player. The bricks must be shared **fairly**, with the same number in each tower. Can you do it? If you can, keep the card. If you can't, put the card back on the bottom of the pile.
❑ Carry on until you have a pile of cards that share fairly and a pile of cards that do not share fairly.
❑ Make a list of the numbers that shared fairly. These are EVEN numbers. Make a list of the numbers that did not share fairly. These are ODD numbers. Take your lists back to school.

BET YOU CAN'T
❑ Work out how many bricks will be in each tower **before** you build them!
❑ Sort out all your 'fair-sharing' cards from the lowest to the highest. What pattern do you notice?

DEAR HELPER

THE POINT OF THIS ACTIVITY: is to introduce your child to **odd and even numbers**. The even numbers to 10 are 2, 4, 6, 8 and 10. Each of these will divide fairly by 2, making two whole numbers. Using bricks of the same size allows your child to build towers and compare them to see whether they are equal.

After a while, your child may not need to build the towers: he or she may be able to use **counting** to compare the amounts. By doing this activity, your child will also be reinforcing his or her ability to count out and recognize numbers up to 10.

YOU MIGHT LIKE TO:
● Remind your child that **even numbers** can always be

paired. Use the image of shoes, which usually come in pairs: 6 shoes make 3 pairs exactly, but 5 shoes make 2 pairs with 1 shoe left over.
● After you have played a few times, spread out the cards face up and let your child choose cards to share fairly. This will tell you whether he or she can now tell which cards are the even numbers.

IF YOU GET STUCK: because your child is having trouble recognizing the numbers or counting the bricks, play with cards up to 6.

Please sign: . . . .

COIN TOSS

YOU WILL NEED: A helper, a pile of 2p coins, a pencil and paper.

YOU ARE GOING TO: use 2p coins to count in twos.
❑ Take five 2p coins. Toss them carefully, one at a time. Which ones land on Heads?
❑ You may keep the Heads coins – BUT you must count how much money that is. So for 3 coins on Heads, count: '2, 4, 6p.' Put the Tails coins back in the pile.
❑ Take turns to do this until all the money has gone.
❑ Can you count up how much money you have scored?

❑ Write down all the numbers from 1 to 10. Draw a circle round each number that you say when you count in 2s with 2ps. Take your list of circled numbers into school.

BET YOU CAN'T
❑ See how high you can count up together in 2s.
❑ Count in 2s backwards from 10 or 20.
❑ Play with 5p coins and count up in 5s.

DEAR HELPER

THE POINT OF THIS ACTIVITY: is to experience counting on in steps of 2. Your child will be counting the **even numbers** up to 20, which are: 2, 4, 6, 8, 10, 12, 14, 16, 18, 20. **Even numbers** are those which divide fairly by 2, making two whole numbers.
   Your child will also be practising adding up and comparing amounts of money. Some children take a long time to grasp that **one** 2p coin is really **two** pence.

YOU MIGHT LIKE TO: Help your child to count in 2s by whispering the 1 and saying the 2 loudly, whispering

the 3 and saying the 4 loudly, and so on. Or you could clap as you say the **even** numbers.

IF YOU GET STUCK:
● Help your child to count the Heads coins in each group of five coins as 2s (see above). Don't worry about counting the final total in 2s.
● Alternatively, you could play with 1p coins and use the game to practise counting in 1s.

Please sign: . . . .

EVERY THIRD

YOU WILL NEED: A helper, a coloured pencil or crayon, the number grids on this page.

YOU ARE GOING TO: look at the number patterns you make when you count in steps of 3.

❏ Choose a grid. Start at 1 and count along the grid, colouring **every third square** until you reach the end.

❏ Talk about what you notice. Try to explain it to your helper. Try reading out all the coloured-in numbers.

❏ Now try the same thing on the other grid. How is this different from what happened the first time? How is it the same?

❏ Take your coloured-in grids back into school and discuss them.

BET YOU CAN'T

❏ Read the coloured-in numbers **backwards**, from the highest to the lowest.

❏ Draw a different number grid and colour in every third square on this.

1	2	3	4	5	6
7	8	9	10	11	12
13	14	15	16	17	18
19	20	21	22	23	24
25	26	27	28	29	30

1	2	3	4	5
6	7	8	9	10
11	12	13	14	15
16	17	18	19	20
21	22	23	24	25

DEAR HELPER

THE POINT OF THIS ACTIVITY: is to introduce and discuss the pattern of counting in 3s from 0. Counting in steps of different sizes is an important part of understanding multiplication as repeatedly adding the same amount. This activity will help your child to develop the ability to recognize and use simple number patterns, which is an important mathematical skill. It is a good idea to practise counting both forwards and backwards.

YOU MIGHT LIKE TO: Encourage your child to predict which number will be coloured in next. Be patient while your child tries to explain the patterns that he or she sees. These may not be the same things that you see – if so, that's perfectly OK.

IF YOU GET STUCK: Count every square along the grid with your child, emphasizing every third square – *1, 2, **3**, 1, 2, **3**, 1, 2, **3**...*

Please sign: . . . .

MULTIPLICATION AND DIVISION

IMPACT

EVERY FIFTH

YOU WILL NEED: A helper, a coloured pencil or crayon, the number grid on this page.

YOU ARE GOING TO: look at the number patterns you make when you count in steps of 5.

❑ Talk with your helper about what 'fifth' means.

❑ Start at 1 and count along the grid, colouring in **every fifth square** until you reach the end.

❑ Talk about what you notice. Try to explain it to your helper. Read out all the coloured-in numbers.

❑ Now try reading the coloured-in numbers **backwards**, from the highest to the lowest.

❑ Take your coloured-in grid back into school and discuss it.

> What does 'fifth' mean?

1	2	3	4	5	6	7	8	9	10
11	12	13	14	15	16	17	18	19	20
21	22	23	24	25	26	27	28	29	30
31	32	33	34	35	36	37	38	39	40
41	42	43	44	45	46	47	48	49	50

BET YOU CAN'T

❑ Let your helper cover one of the coloured-in numbers, then tell him or her which one is hidden.

❑ Draw a different number grid and colour in every fifth square on it.

DEAR HELPER

THE POINT OF THIS ACTIVITY: is to introduce and discuss the pattern of counting in 5s from 0. Counting in steps of different sizes is an important part of understanding multiplication as repeatedly adding the same amount. This activity will help your child to develop the ability to recognize and use simple number patterns, which is an important mathematical skill. It is a good idea to practise counting both forwards and backwards.

YOU MIGHT LIKE TO: Encourage your child to

predict which number will be coloured in next. Be patient while your child tries to explain the patterns he or she sees. These may not be the same things that you see, but that is perfectly OK.

IF YOU GET STUCK: Count every square along the grid with your child, emphasizing every fifth square – 1, 2, 3, 4, **5**, 1, 2, 3, 4, **5**...

Please sign: . . . .

MY CALENDAR

YOU WILL NEED: A helper; the calendar on page 40; a pencil; some coloured pencils (red, yellow and green).

YOU ARE GOING TO: make a calendar for your birthday month.

❑ Write the name of your birthday month at the top of the calendar sheet.

❑ Each space is for one day. The first space is the 1st of the month. Can you find **the right space for your birthday**?

❑ Write it in – using ordinary pencil in case you need to move it! When you are sure it is the right space, colour it in green.

❑ Find out which day of the week the 1st is.

❑ Now find all the **Saturdays** and colour them in yellow. Write SAT on each one.

❑ Now find all the **Sundays** and colour them in red. Write SUN on each one.

❑ Talk about what you notice.

❑ Now number all the days in your month. How many days are there in your birthday month? Cross out the spaces you don't need.

❑ Take your completed birthday month back to school to help make a class year calendar.

BET YOU CAN'T

❑ Find out which day of the week your birthday is on.

❑ Write in any other important events in your birthday month.

It's my birthday too!

DEAR HELPER

THE POINT OF THIS ACTIVITY: is to help your child recognize and use the sequence of days in the week. He or she will also be practising counting, reading and writing the numbers from 1 to 30.

YOU MIGHT LIKE TO: Look at the completed month calendar with your child and ask questions such as *What comes after 17?, What number comes next?* or *Find a number between 17 and 20.* Read all the numbers in order from 1 to 30, and then from 30 down to 1, aloud together.

IF YOU GET STUCK:
● If your child finds it difficult to remember the order of

the numbers, try using a tape measure as a reference.
● It is worth remembering that in our counting system, the numbers do not always sound as they ought to! In particular, the 'teens' numbers can be difficult to understand because they are said 'backwards' ('sixteen' instead of 'teen-six'). Also, it can be hard to distinguish between numbers such as 13 and 30 when they are spoken aloud.
● If your child finds **writing** a number difficult, ask him or her to tell you what to write and then write it down for him or her. It will still be your child who is doing the mathematics!

Please sign: . . . .

MULTISTEP AND MIXED OPERATIONS

IMPACT

IMPACT PHOTOCOPIABLE

MY CALENDAR

The month is:

6 SPOTS

YOU WILL NEED: A helper, a set of dominoes.

YOU ARE GOING TO: find pairs of numbers making 6 and play a hiding game.

❏ Spread out the dominoes so that you can see them all.

❏ Now you have to match the domino ends so that you make a total of 6 spots each time, like this:

❏ Can you use up all the dominoes to make a complete ring of 6s?

❏ When the ring is finished, close your eyes while your helper removes one domino. When you open your eyes, can you work out which domino is hidden? Take turns to play this hiding game.

❏ Back at school, be ready to talk about what you have done.

BET YOU CAN'T

Ask your helper to remove a domino and tell you the ends on both sides of the gap – then you have to work out the missing domino **without** opening your eyes! This is more tricky than it sounds!

DEAR HELPER

THE POINT OF THIS ACTIVITY: is to practise addition involving numbers up to 6 by solving a simple mathematical puzzle. When you remove a domino from the ring, your child has to work out which one it is. To do this, he or she needs to use the pattern of the domino line and choose an appropriate operation (probably subtraction) to solve the problem. Try it yourself and see how you do it!

YOU MIGHT LIKE TO:
● Play more than once. Is a different ring possible?
● Discourage your child from counting every spot by

saying the number of spots on the end already placed (for example, 'FOUR') and getting him or her to count on the spots from there: 'FOUR, 5, 6!'

IF YOU GET STUCK:
● Take out all the dominoes above (4, 4) and make a line with pairs of ends that total 4.
● Make a traditional domino ring with matching ends, then remove one domino for your child to identify.

Please sign: . . . .

MULTISTEP AND MIXED OPERATIONS

IMPACT

COIN FEEL

YOU WILL NEED: A helper, a cloth or paper bag, a collection of different coins.

YOU ARE GOING TO: see whether you can recognize a coin by feeling it.
❑ Put all the coins in the bag and shake them up.
❑ Close your eyes and put your hand into the bag. Pick up a coin and feel it. Can you say which coin it is?
❑ Open your eyes. Were you right? Put the coin down outside the bag.
❑ Now it is your helper's turn. If either of you gets a coin wrong, it goes back in the bag.
❑ Carry on until the bag is empty. Can you work out how much money each of you has collected?
❑ Back at school, be ready to talk about the differences between the coins. Which ones are easy to tell apart? Which ones are harder?

This one's got straight edges.

BET YOU CAN'T
❑ Put your coins in order, from the one worth most to the one worth least.
❑ Find a coin as quickly as possible when your helper says – for example: *Find a 10p, GO!*

DEAR HELPER

THE POINT OF THIS ACTIVITY: is to be able to recognize the different coins and remember what they are worth. Your child will also be practising adding up an amount of money.

YOU MIGHT LIKE TO: Look at the coins very carefully, comparing the 'Heads' and 'Tails' sides and discussing what each coin is worth, before you start.

IF YOU GET STUCK:
Put a smaller selection of coins in the bag, perhaps starting with 1p and 2p coins only.

Please sign: . . . .

MULTISTEP AND MIXED OPERATIONS

IMPACT

COIN RUB

YOU WILL NEED: A helper, paper and crayons, Blu-tack, a collection of different coins.

YOU ARE GOING TO: look carefully at some different coins and make a picture with them.

❑ Secretly choose a coin. Put a small piece of Blu-tack on the table to hold the coin still, Heads side up.

❑ Put a sheet of paper over the Blu-tacked coin. Holding the coin as still as you can, crayon gently over it. How quickly can your helper tell you which coin it is?

❑ Now it is your helper's turn to rub a hidden coin.

❑ Take turns until you have rubbed all the different coins between you.

❑ Try rubbing the Tails side of some coins. Is it easier to tell which coin it is from the Tails side or from the Heads side?

❑ Choose and rub some coins to make a picture. Can you work out how much your coin picture is worth?

❑ Take your paper with the coin rubbings back to school.

BET YOU CAN'T
Rub a coin picture that is worth exactly 20p.

DEAR HELPER

THE POINT OF THIS ACTIVITY: is to reinforce your child's ability to recognize different coins and remember what each coin is worth. Your child will also be practising adding up a collection of mixed coins.

YOU MIGHT LIKE TO:
● Discuss the value of each coin and order the coins by their value.
● Discuss easy ways of adding up coin values before

you start – for example, starting with the largest-value coin and adding on to that.

IF YOU GET STUCK:
Limit the range of coins your child uses in his or her coin picture to just 2p and 1p coins. This will make the totalling easier.

Please sign: . . . .

MULTISTEP AND MIXED OPERATIONS

IMPACT

MAKE 10P

YOU WILL NEED: A helper; some 10p, 2p and 1p pieces.

YOU ARE GOING TO: play a game making 10p with 2p and 1p coins.
❑ The aim is to make 10p in the purse. To do this, you take turns to put a coin in the purse.

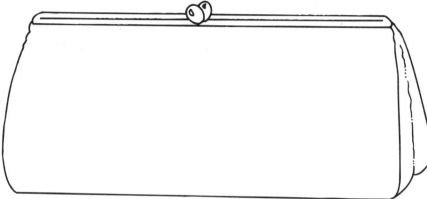

TO PLAY:
❑ Put all the coins in a pile **outside** the purse.
❑ Decide who will start. If you start, you may put **either a 2p coin or a 1p coin** in the purse.
❑ Now your helper takes a turn to put either a 2p or a 1p in the purse.
❑ Now it is your turn again – what will you add this time? **Think about** how much money is in the purse already.
❑ When one of you makes the money in the purse up to exactly 10p, empty the purse and exchange all the coins for one 10p piece. The player who has made the purse up to 10p keeps the 10p piece!
❑ Play until the 10p pieces run out. How much money has each of you scored?
❑ Back at school, be ready to talk about what happened and how you played the game.

BET YOU CAN'T
❑ See what happens if you can add 1p, 2p **or 3p** when it is your turn.
❑ See what happens if you introduce a **5p** piece into the game.

DEAR HELPER

THE POINT OF THIS ACTIVITY: is for your child to practise adding more than two numbers together, using money. At the same time, he or she will have to decide which is the best amount to add on. You will need to play the game several times for your child to be able to come up with a winning strategy. You will also be counting in 10s together as you add up how much you have each won.

In addition, your child will be experiencing the principle of **exchange** in relation to money. He or she will understand that one 2p coin is worth the same as two 1p coins, and that you can exchange a collection of 1p and 2p coins fairly for one 10p coin.

YOU MIGHT LIKE TO:
● Help your child add on the 2p coins by encouraging him or her to 'tap' the 2p twice with a finger as you count.
● Tell your child to move and sort out the coins within the purse for easier counting up.

IF YOU GET STUCK: Try playing the game using only 1p coins. You can still put either 1p or 2p (two 1p coins) in the purse. Some children take a long time to understand that **one** 2p coin is really **two** pence.

Please sign: . . . .

HIDDEN MONEY

YOU WILL NEED: A helper; a collection of 1p, 2p and 5p coins.

YOU ARE GOING TO: use your head to work out a hidden amount of money!
❏ Together, choose a few coins to lay on the table. Work out how much is there. **Hold this number in your head!**
❏ Now close your eyes while your helper hides some of the coins.
❏ Open your eyes and look at how much money is left. Can you say how much is hidden?
❏ Play a number of times, taking turns to hide the money.
❏ Change the total when you are both ready.

There's 8p here...

❏ When you are good at working out how much money is missing, try this! **Before** you open your eyes, your helper tells you how much money is left on the table. You must say how much money is hidden while your eyes are still closed. Then open your eyes and see whether you were right! Play again, taking turns.
❏ Back at school, be ready to play some more mental money games.
❏ Think about how you worked out some of your answers.

BET YOU CAN'T
❏ Explain to your helper how you are working out the answers.
❏ Play again, but start from a different total each time (this is **much** trickier).

DEAR HELPER

THE POINT OF THIS ACTIVITY: is to practise mental arithmetic, and to solve a problem using money. The game is challenging, and it is important for your child to be successful at it. Give him or her lots of encouragement and support (see below).

YOU MIGHT LIKE TO:
● Ask your child to hide the coins first, and talk to him or her about how you are working out the hidden amount.

● Start with the same total (for example, 5p) each time and change the amount you hide. Make the total in several different ways.

IF YOU GET STUCK:
● Play the game with 1p coins only. Start with the same total each time, then work towards changing the total number of 1p coins each time.

Please sign: . . . .

MAKE A RECTANGLE

YOU WILL NEED: A helper, a pack of playing cards with all the cards over 5 taken out (the Ace counts as 1), a pencil and paper.

YOU MIGHT LIKE TO TRY: use cards to make an addition rectangle!

❑ Shuffle the pack of cards. Take the top six cards and lay them out to make a rectangle, like this:

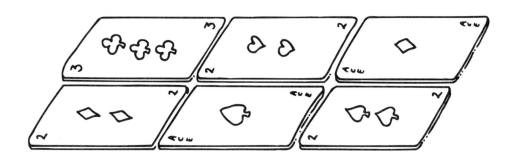

❑ How many points is your rectangle worth? Add up the values of the six cards to find out. (Remember the Ace counts as 1.) Record the total. Put the cards aside.

❑ Lay out six new cards. Is this rectangle worth more or fewer points?

❑ Carry on until you have used all the cards.

❑ Back at school, you will be talking about the easiest ways to add up numbers. Talk about this with your helper.

❑ Draw around the cards in one of your rectangles. Write in the six card values, and write the total underneath. Take this into school.

BET YOU CAN'T

Work out the largest total and the smallest total that you could make a rectangle worth, using these cards.

DEAR HELPER

THE POINT OF THIS ACTIVITY: is to practise adding more than two numbers, and to understand that you can add numbers in any order. Encourage your child to look at the numbers on the cards **before** he or she starts adding them up. Can your child find and use a pair of numbers that he or she knows by heart (for example, a double or a pair of numbers that total 5 or 10)? Alternatively, can he or she find the largest number and add on to it?

YOU MIGHT LIKE TO:

● Remind your child that he or she can reorganize the cards to make them easier to add up. Compare and discuss different ways of adding.

● Try adding the numbers while your child adds them in a different order, then checking that you agree.

● Discourage your child from counting the symbols (hearts, clubs and so on) on the cards by talking about the **numbers**.

IF YOU GET STUCK: Use the 1, 2 and 3 cards only (you might like to use two packs for this).

Please sign: . . . .

RACING TRACKS

PHOTOCOPIABLE

Start

My track

Start

My helper's track

IMPACT

MENTAL MATHS HOMEWORK

Dear Parent

We all know that parents are a crucial factor in their children's learning. You can make a huge difference to your child's education. We are planning to send home some activities that fit in with the maths we are doing in school. The activities are designed for your child to do with you, or another available adult. You do not need to know a lot of maths in order to help your child.

These are not traditional homework activities. It is important your child first explains the activity to you. Each activity will have been explained thoroughly in school. Then do the activity together. By sharing these activities with your child, you will be helping to develop her or his mental maths. And as a result of being given that all-important attention, your child is more likely to become confident and skilled in maths.

We hope, too, that these activities will be fun to do – it matters that children develop positive attitudes to maths. If you are particularly nervous about maths, try not to make your child nervous too! If your child is having difficulties, look at the 'If you get stuck' suggestions which are provided on each activity sheet.

After completing each activity, your child will usually have something to bring back to school. However, sometimes there may not be anything written down to bring back – your child is doing mental maths, so all the work may be in your heads!

If you have any problems with or further questions about any of the activities – or about any of the maths being covered – please do let us know at school. We do very much value your support.

Yours sincerely

MENTAL MATHS HOMEWORK